THIS PAWSOME BOOK BELONGS TO:

_____

PAW Patrol™: 2020

A CENTUM BOOK 978-1-913072-36-0

Published in Great Britain by Centum Books Ltd

This edition published 2019

1 3 5 7 9 10 8 6 4 2

Centum Books Ltd, 20 Devon Square, Newton Abbot, Devon, TQ12 2HR, UK

books@centumbooksltd.co.uk

CENTUM BOOKS Limited Reg. No. 07641486

A CIP catalogue record for this book is available from the British Library

Printed in Poland.

2020

centum

CONTENTS

WELCOME TO ADVENTURE BAY!

High paw, pup fans! Get ready for puzzle missions and activity challenges in every corner of Adventure Bay. Chase, Marshall, Skye and all the pups are here to help, so put your best paw forward and LET'S GET STARTED.

Are you RUFF-RUFF READY?

POLICE CONE HUNT!

Help police pup Chase sniff out 6 cones hidden on pages throughout the book! **Tick them below as you track them down.**

It's an Emergency!

Ryder's PupPad has just beeped with an urgent message. What does it say? **Use the code to find out – quick!**

CODE KEY

C	E	I	M	N	O	R	S	T	U	V	W	K

Who sent the message to Ryder?
Unscramble the letters.

K E J A

_ _ _ _

Pup Search

All paws on deck! Gather the pups by finding their names in the grid. **Look forward, back, up, down and diagonally.**

B	C	H	A	S	E	B	E	W	Y
H	J	X	U	C	V	S	L	K	S
S	L	M	Z	B	A	Y	C	A	K
T	L	A	S	Z	B	O	X	H	Y
R	A	R	C	R	U	B	B	L	E
A	H	S	W	Q	Y	M	E	Z	X
C	S	H	D	H	T	E	A	U	M
K	R	A	R	C	S	A	R	M	F
E	A	L	A	Y	K	C	O	R	O
R	M	L	W	X	J	X	O	Y	G

CHASE

MARSHALL

SKYE

RUBBLE

ROCKY

ZUMA

Can you **find** a jungle pup hiding in the grid, too?

ANSWERS ON **PAGE 51**

9

Profile: RYDER

The PAW Patrol is on the job!

NAME: Ryder

AGE: 10

ROLE: Leader of the *PAW Patrol*

GADGETS: PupPad

VEHICLE: ATV, which has a Hovercraft mode and Snowmobile mode

SKILLS: Pup training, problem-solving, gadget fixing

CATCHPHRASE:
'No job is too BIG, no pup is too SMALL!'

DID YOU KNOW?

Ryder's jacket is a high-tech gadget, too! **It can transform into a life jacket during water missions.**

Let's Draw Ryder!

Ryder's on a roll. **Copy the picture of the PAW Patrol leader, using the grid to guide you.**

Now colour Ryder so he's ready for the next adventure!

LET'S GET MIGHTY!

A meteor has landed in Adventure Bay and given the pups mysterious powers! **Help the Mighty Pups on their missions to save the day.**

SUPER SLEDGE

Which path will lead Mighty Everest down the mountain to a soft, snowy landing?

IN A SPIN

Cross out every second letter and then write the remaining letters below to reveal Chase's Mighty power.

_ _ _ _ _ _ _ _ _ _ _

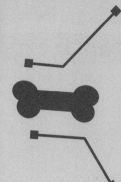

PUP PAIRS

Draw lines to match the Mighty Pup pairs.
Which pup doesn't have a match?

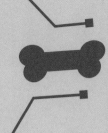

ANSWERS ON **PAGE 51**

13

Pups Save a Baby Octopus

Mayor Goodway is planning a party to celebrate the opening of Adventure Beach. She asks the *PAW Patrol* to be the Lifeguard Rescue Team.
"Today, we are the *SEA Patrol!*" says Ryder.

Out on the water, Cap'n Turbot is feeding Wally the Walrus some jellyfish jerky. Spying the treats, a baby octopus swims away from its mum, gobbles one up and climbs aboard the Flounder.

In search of her baby, the mumma octopus swims under the Flounder and wraps her tentacles around it. "Slithering sea serpents!" cries Cap'n Turbot. He calls Ryder's PupPad.

SEA Patrol to the rescue! Zuma jets over to the Flounder in his special boat and uses its grabbers to tickle the tentacles. They release the Flounder and slip back into the sea.

But, oh no ... **where has Baby Octopus gone?**

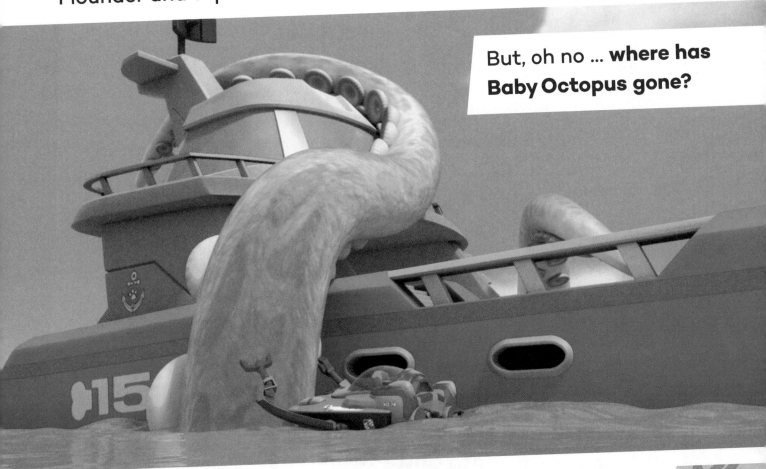

CONTINUED ON **PAGE 28**

Profile: CHASE

His NOSE knows!

NAME: Chase

BREED: German Shepherd

ROLE: Police pup

UNIFORM COLOUR: Blue

GADGETS: Pup Pack with megaphone, searchlight and a net that can shoot out to catch things

VEHICLE: Police truck

SKILLS: Directing traffic, blocking dangers, solving mysteries

CATCHPHRASE:

CHASE IS ON THE CASE!

DID YOU KNOW?

Chase can sniff out anything – **but he's allergic to cats and feathers!**

16

Where's Chase?

Chase is hiding. **Can you find him in the grid?**

Tick off these items as you spot them.

Chase's bowl

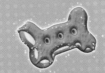

Bone pup treat

Chase's badge

ANSWERS ON **PAGE 51**

Profile: MARSHALL

He's all fired up!

NAME: Marshall

BREED: Dalmatian

ROLE: Fire pup and Medic pup

UNIFORM COLOUR: Red

GADGETS:
Pup Pack with a double-spray fire hose

VEHICLE: Fire engine

SKILLS: Putting out fires, rescuing animals, medical help

CATCHPHRASE:

READY FOR A RUFF-RUFF RESCUE!

DID YOU KNOW?

Marshall's medical supplies include an X-ray screen to check pups and people for injuries!

Spot the Pairs

Match the Marshalls! **Draw lines to connect the spotted Dalmatian pairs.**

Trace Marshall's pup tag and give it some FIERY COLOUR.

ANSWERS ON **PAGE 51**

Profile: SKYE

Pups away!

NAME: Skye

BREED: Cockapoo

ROLE: Pilot pup

UNIFORM COLOUR: Pink

GADGETS: Pup Pack with wings that allow her to take flight

VEHICLE: Helicopter

SKILLS: Flying, flips and spins!

CATCHPHRASE:

THIS PUP'S GOTTA FLY!

DID YOU KNOW?

Skye is really brave and very little frightens her, but one thing she is afraid of is eagles.

Dot-to-dot-apoo!

Join the dots to reveal your favourite Cockapoo as she soars through the sky.

DOODLE some clouds and birds in the sky around the pup.

Pups at Play

Pups that play together, stay together! **Can you match the missing jigsaw pieces to the scene?**

How many rabbits can you spot in the picture?

1 2 3 4 5

MIGHTY COLOURING!

The Mighty Pups have a mysterious mission in Adventure Bay. **Colour them in.**

Profile: RUBBLE

Let's dig it!

NAME: Rubble

BREED: Bulldog

ROLE: Construction pup

UNIFORM COLOUR: Yellow

GADGETS: Pup Pack with a bucket arm scoop

VEHICLE: Digger with a bucket shovel and drill

SKILLS: Building, digging, lifting and transporting heavy things

CATCHPHRASE:

HERE COMES RUBBLE, ON THE DOUBLE!

DID YOU KNOW?

Rubble loves to get covered in mud and then visit Katie's Pet Parlour for a warm bubble bath!

I Can Dig It!

A road is blocked with big boulders. **No trouble, just call Rubble!**

How many boulders does he still need to move?

Can you spot this rock in the pile?

There are ☐ boulders.

ANSWERS ON **PAGE 52**

27

Pups Save a Baby Octopus

Part 2

Read Part 1
on **pages 14-15**

On Adventure Beach the party is in full swing. Nobody spots a little, quiet guest gobbling up the plates of food ... the baby octopus!

Mumma Octopus comes looking for her baby, but she starts grabbing all the wrong things! Skye parasails through the air to distract Mumma Octopus and Rubble builds a wall of sand to protect the people.

"How will we ever stop this ferocious beast?" Mayor Goodway gasps. But Ryder realises Mumma Octopus is not ferocious, she's worried. He spots Baby Octopus on Mayor Humdinger's head. "That's it!" Ryder cries. **"This must be the big octopus's baby!"**

The Sea Patrol reunite Mumma Octopus and her baby, who she sweeps up in her tentacles for a hug ...

... and Ryder presents the brave pups with their lifeguard badges. *Go SEA Patrol!*

Profile: ROCKY

Rocky to the rescue!

NAME: Rocky

BREED: Mixed breed

ROLE: Recycling pup

UNIFORM COLOUR: Green

GADGETS: Pup Pack with a mechanical claw and lots of handy tools

VEHICLE: Recycling truck

SKILLS: Creativity and ideas, fixing things, solving problems

CATCHPHRASE:

DON'T LOSE IT – REUSE IT!

DID YOU KNOW?

Rocky doesn't like getting wet at all, **which means bath time isn't much fun!**

Don't Lose It!

Rocky is sorting his recycling into groups. **Pick out the green bottles and write the letters on the lines below to read his mystery message.**

__ __ __ __ __ __
__ __ __ __ __ __ __ __

Unscramble the letters on the red bottles to reveal a special friend!

__ __ __ __ __

ANSWERS ON **PAGE 52**

To the Rescue

Pick the items you would choose for these pup-tastic challenges.

1 Ryder needs to get a message to the pups quickly. **What would work best?**

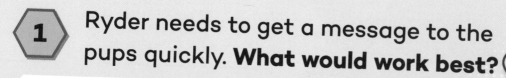
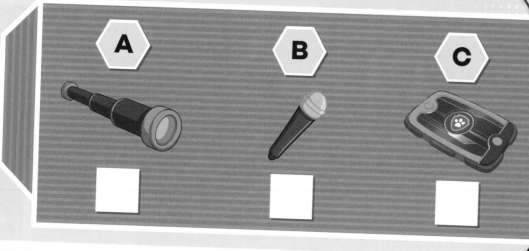

A

B

C

2 Rocky needs to fix some dangerously loose nails in a go-kart. **What does he need from his pack?**

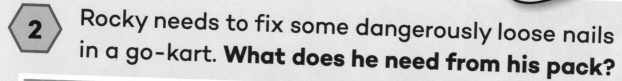

A

B

C

3

Help! The pups have an emergency in deep snow.
Which vehicle can get there?

A ☐

B ☐   C ☐

4

Cali is stuck in a tall tree and only Marshall can help.
What item should he bring?

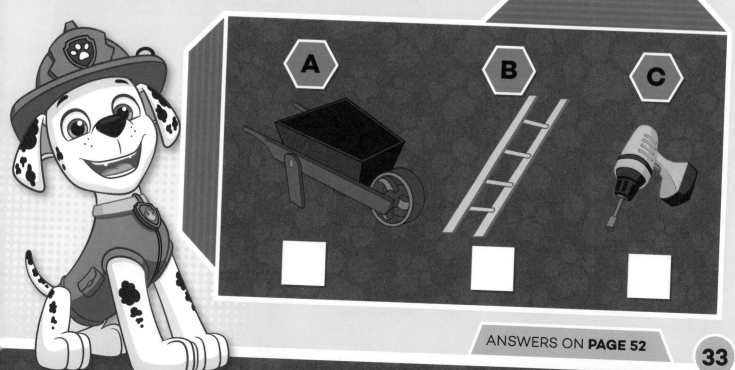

A   B   C

☐   ☐   ☐

ANSWERS ON **PAGE 52**

Race to Ryder

Get ruff-ruff ready for this PAW Patrol board game!

Ryder has a special mission for you!
But first you need to get to the Lookout.
Who will be the first to round up
all the pups and reach the finish?

You will need:

- 2-4 players
- A coin counter for each player
- A dice

START HERE

1

2

3 — *CHASE* is in his police uniform, ready to go! **MOVE FORWARD 5 SPACES**

4

5 — *RUBBLE* has a road block to complete. **MOVE BACK 1 SPACE**

6

7 — Wheeee! *EVEREST* is busy snowboarding. **MISS A TURN**

8

9

10

11 — *MARSHALL* is all fired up. **TAKE A SHORTCUT TO SQUARE 16!**

12

13

What to do:

- Place your coins on the **START** square.
- Take turns to roll the dice. Whoever is first to roll a 6 begins.
- Roll the dice and move that number of spaces on the board.
- If you land on an Action square, follow the instructions.
- The first to land on the **FINISH** square is the winner!

14

15

16

17

18

19

20

21

Uh-oh!
ZUMA has an
emergency at sea.
**MOVE BACK
3 SPACES**

22

23

24

SKYE'S helicopter
has got you
in a spin!
**CHOOSE SOMEONE
TO SWAP PLACES
WITH YOU**

25

26

ROCKY'S tools are
ready for action.
**MOVE FORWARD
1 SPACE**

27

28

FINISH

35

Profile: ZUMA

Let's dive in!

NAME: Zuma

BREED: Labrador

ROLE: Water-rescue pup

UNIFORM COLOUR: Orange

GADGETS: Pup Pack with air tanks and propellers for diving and swimming underwater

VEHICLE: Hovercraft that can travel on land or water

SKILLS: Rescuing sea animals, underwater missions, water sports

CATCHPHRASE:

READY, SET, GET WET!

DID YOU KNOW?

Zuma's hovercraft can transform into a **submarine** for deep underwater adventures!

Colour Splash

Dive in and draw the other half of Zuma's face.
Awesome work, dude!

Now COPY THE COLOURS so he's a perfect match!

Are you ready for some more super-charged puzzles? **Prepare to save the day!**

COUNT ON SKYE

Mighty Skye has put the wind in a spin and is zooming through the air! **How many times does she appear?**

JUST THE OPPOSITE

The Mighty Pups' powers make them faster, stronger and tougher than ever. **What words are the opposite of the words below?**

FAST.............................. WET..............................

STRONG........................ HEAVY..........................

TOP.............................. SHALLOW.......................

SUPER SUDOKU

Write the correct pups' names in the blank squares to complete the grids. **Each Mighty Pup shown on the grid should appear three times, and only once in each column and row.**

ANSWERS ON **PAGE 52**

39

Profile: EVEREST

Born to slide!

NAME: Everest

BREED: Husky

ROLE: Mountain-rescue pup

UNIFORM COLOUR: Turquoise and yellow

GADGETS: Pup Pack with a grappling hook and foldable, rocket-powered snowboard

VEHICLE: Snow plough with a claw to grab large objects, and transport a sledge

SKILLS: Snowy rescues, climbing icy slopes, super-fast snowboarding

CATCHPHRASE:

ICE OR SNOW, I'M READY TO GO!

DID YOU KNOW?

Everest likes **belly-bogganing**, where she slides down the slopes on her belly!

Word Slide

Solve the clues to this slippery word game and get Everest to the bottom of the slope.

1 It forms when water freezes.

2 It falls from the sky when it's very cold.

3 Everest is this breed of dog.

4 Sit on it to slide down a snowy hill.

5 The place where Everest lives with Jake.

6 Everest has a rocket-powered one for extra-fast sliding!

Profile: TRACKER

Buenos dias, PAW Patrol!

NAME: Tracker

BREED: Chihuahua

ROLE: Jungle-rescue pup

UNIFORM COLOUR: Green

GADGETS: Pup Pack with a compass, torch and grappling cables

VEHICLE: Jeep with a special radar tracking system

SKILLS: Jungle rescues, super-hearing (thanks to his big ears!)

CATCHPHRASE:

I'M ALL EARS!

DID YOU KNOW?

Tracker can speak two languages – **English and Spanish.**

42

Track the PAWprints

Tracker is following a set of paw prints through the rainforest. **Help him along the trail to find his way to the mystery pup!**

START →

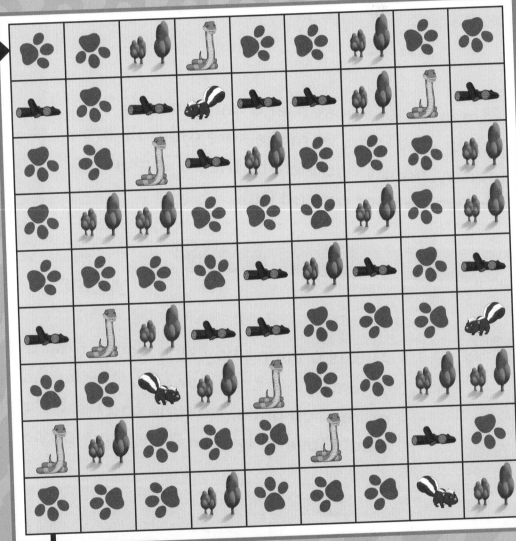

↓

FINISH

Which pup is Tracker tailing?

HINT: This spy pup would usually be the one doing the tracking!

ANSWERS ON **PAGE 53**

Profiles:

Ryder and the PAW Patrol do everything they can to keep their friends safe. **Meet some more of the Adventure Bay gang!**

PATROL FRIENDS

KATIE

Katie is Ryder's best friend and runs the Pet Parlour. **She loves to make sure animals are healthy, happy and well-bathed – including her own pet cat named Cali.**

ALEX

Alex is a young boy who doesn't always pay attention, so the PAW Patrol have rescued him more than once! **He runs the Mini-Patrol and would love to be like Ryder one day.**

MR PORTER

Mr Porter is a restaurant owner in Adventure Bay, and also Alex's grandfather. **He's kind, wise and caring towards others.**

JAKE

Jake is a mountain ranger who lives in a snowy chalet and loves to snowboard. **He looks after Everest and knows a lot about animals such as penguins and deer.**

MAYOR GOODWAY

Mayor Goodway is the mayor of Adventure Bay, proudly following in the footsteps of her great-great-great-great-grandfather, Grover Goodway, the first mayor of the town. **She has a pet chicken called Chickaletta.**

FARMER YUMI

Farmer Yumi lives on Fuji Farm and looks after the crops and animals. **The pups often help her out on the farm and she is also their Pup-Fu sensei.**

WALLY

Wally is a walrus who lives in The Bay. **He is a talented walrus who loves food, so he enjoys doing tricks for Cap'n Turbot in return for treats!**

Spot the Kit-astrophe!

The Kitty Catastrophe Crew from Foggy Bottom have come to cause trouble for the pups!
Spot eight differences.

Colour a paw for every difference you spot.

Ruff-Ruff Race

The pups are holding a special Pup Games, and only one can win the first place ribbon. **Which pup is the winner of the race?**

Which pup comes **4th?**

....

ANSWERS ON **PAGE 53**

Pup-tastic Quiz!

Are you a **PAW Patrol** superfan? **Pick a pup for each answer in this PAWsome quiz.**

1   **Which pup** wears a **yellow uniform?**

....

2   **Which pup** has the strongest sense of smell?

....

3   **Which pup** lives on **Jake's Mountain?**

....

48

4 Which pup can be a little clumsy?

....

5 Which pup likes to fly high in her **helicopter?**

....

6 Which pup has an anchor on his pup tag?

....

7 Which pup loves to say, **'Green Means Go!'?**

....

Now check your answers and turn over to find your **superfan score!**

ANSWERS ON **PAGE 53**

How many answers did you get right?

0-3 correct

Practice makes PAWfect

Get fired up and learn a little more about the pups by trying all the quizzes in this book!

4-6 correct

Itching to know more

Good job. Now, dive back into this book and soon you will have an even more PAWsome score!

7 correct

Totally PAWsome!

Nobody could know more about the **PAW Patrol** than you. You're on a roll!

HIGH PAW!

Answers

Did you find all the hidden cones? They can be found on pages **10, 17, 23, 27, 36,** and **49.**

PAGE 8

Everest stuck in snow storm, JAKE.

PAGE 9

```
B C H A S E B E W Y
H J X U C V S L K S
S L M Z B A Y C A K
T L A S Z B O X H Y
R A R C R U B B L E
A H S W Q Y M E Z X
C S H D H T E A U M
K R A R C S A R M F
E A L A Y K C O R O
R M L W X J X O Y G
```

Tracker is also in the grid.

PAGES 12-13

1. Path B, **2.** Super speed,
3. Rocky doesn't have a match.

PAGE 17

PAGE 19

51

PAGES 22-23

There are 6 rabbits.

PAGE 27
21 boulders.

PAGE 31
GREEN MEANS GO,
Ryder.

PAGES 32-33
1. C, **2.** B, **3.** A, **4.** B.

PAGES 38-39
1. 14 times,
2. Fast/Slow,
Strong/Weak, Top/Bottom,
Wet/Dry, Heavy/Light,
Shallow/Deep,

3.

PAGE 41

1. Ice, **2.** Snow, **3.** Husky, **4.** Sledge, **5.** Mountain, **6.** Snowboard.

PAGE 43

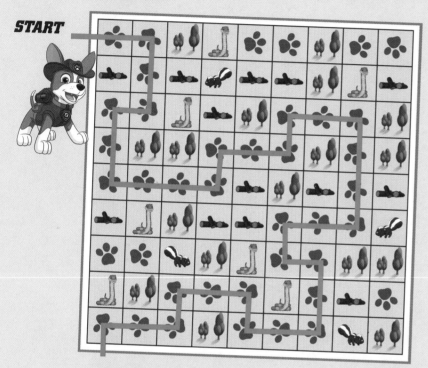

START

FINISH

Tracker is trailing Chase.

PAGE 47

Marshall is the winner, Rubble comes 4th.

PAGES 48-49

1. Rubble,
2. Chase,
3. Everest,
4. Marshall,
5. Skye,
6. Zuma,
7. Rocky.

PAGE 46